Discover the Lead

CLARINET

Kids' Film & T.V. Themes

Series Editor: Anna Joyce
Production Editor: Chris Harvey
Editorial, production and recording: Artemis Music Limited • Design and production: Space DPS Limited • Published 2001

IMP
International MUSIC Publications

Introduction

Welcome to DISCOVER THE LEAD, part of an instrumental series that provides beginners of all ages with fun, alternative material to increase their repertoire, but overall, enjoyment of their instrument!

For those of you just starting out, the idea of solo playing may sound rather daunting. DISCOVER THE LEAD will help you develop reading and playing skills, while increasing your confidence as a soloist.

You will find that the eight well-known songs have been carefully selected and arranged at an easy level - although interesting and musically satisfying. You will also notice that the arrangements can be used along with all the instruments in the series – flute, clarinet, alto saxophone, tenor saxophone, trumpet, violin and piano – making group playing possible!

The professionally recorded backing CD allows you to hear each song in two different ways:
- a complete demonstration performance with solo + backing
- backing only, so you can play along and DISCOVER THE LEAD!

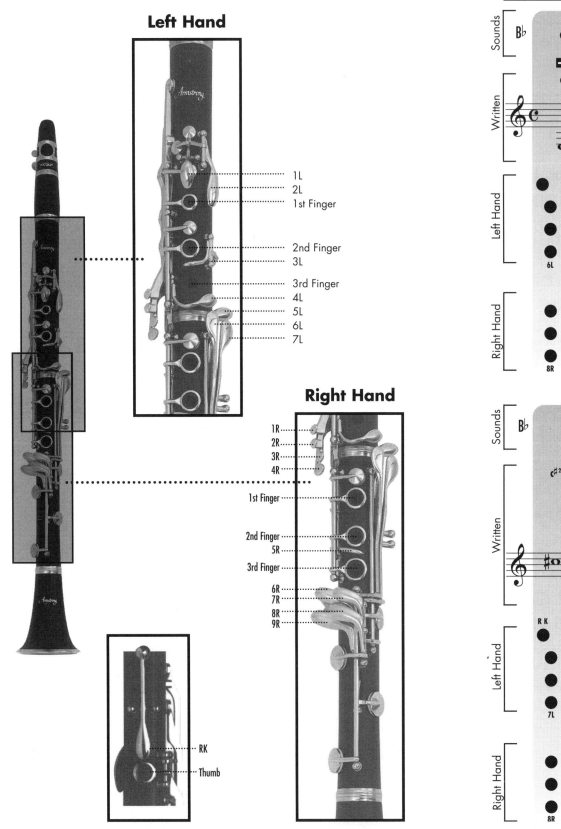

Left Hand

Right Hand

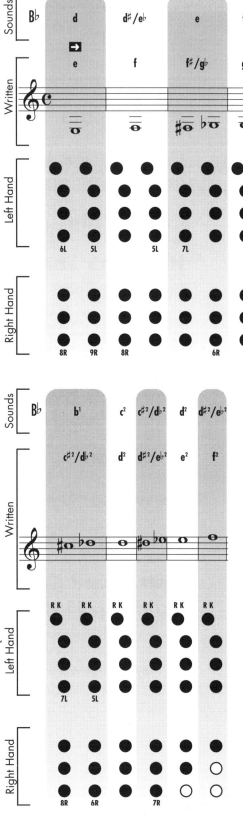

Wherever possible we have simplified the more tricky rhythms and melodies, but if you are in any doubt listen to the complete performance tracks and follow the style of the players. Also, we have kept marks of expression to a minimum, but feel free to experiment with these – but above all, have fun!

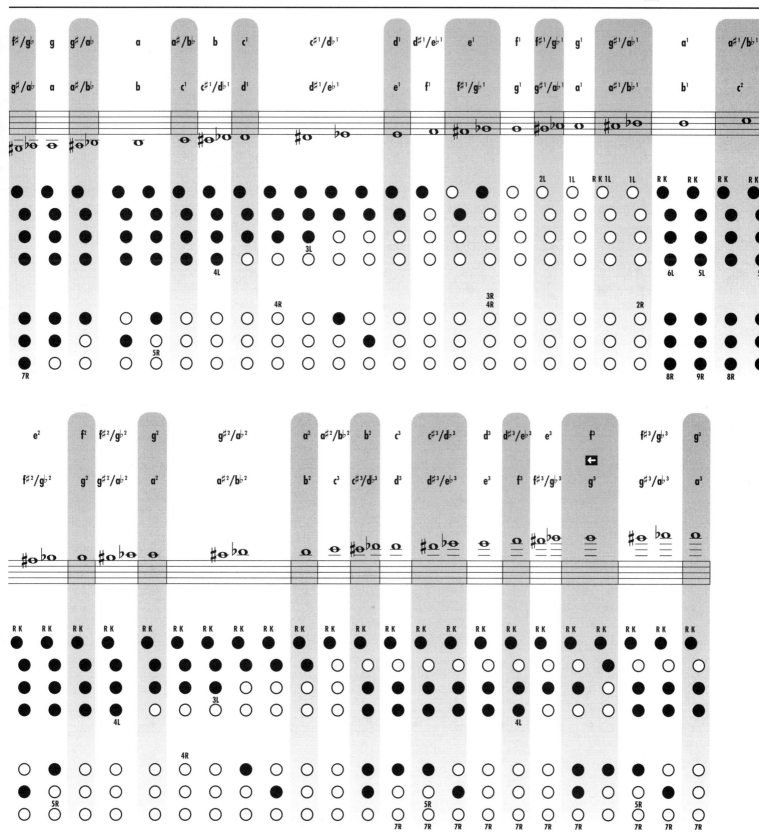

Indicates the lower limit of the best playing range for B♭ Clarinets

Indicates the upper limit of the best playing range for B♭ Clarinets

Animaniacs

Demonstration

Backing

Words by Tom Ruegger
Music by Richard Stone

Brightly

Can We Fix It?
from Bob The Builder

Demonstration

Backing

Words and Music by Paul Joyce

Chitty Chitty Bang Bang

Demonstration

Backing

Words and Music by
Richard Sherman and Robert Sherman

Hedwig's Theme
from Harry Potter And The Philosopher's Stone

Music by John Williams

Demonstration

Backing

Number One
as performed by the Tweenies

Words and Music by
Nicholas Coler and Henrik Korpi

Over The Rainbow
from The Wizard Of Oz

Words by E Y Harburg
Music by Harold Arlen

Pokémon

Demonstration   Backing

Words and Music by
John Siegler and Tamara Loeffler

New Scooby Doo Mysteries

Demonstration

Backing

Words and Music by Joseph Barbera,
William Hanna and Hoyt Curtin

Care Of Your Clarinet

Things You Should Have

Cork grease or Vaseline
Medium bristle artist's paint brush
Weighted cloth swab for inside
Two cloths, one for the outside and one for the mouthpiece
Key oil
At least one extra reed

Putting Your Clarinet Together

The Clarinet keys and rods cross over the sections and can be easily damaged, so assemble it very gently. You can use a little cork grease or Vaseline to help when putting it together.

Hold the upper section so that the bridging is raised and take the lower section and use a twisting motion to insert them together.

If you are having problems playing the low register make sure that you have aligned your Clarinet properly. This will allow the pads to completely cover the holes.

Storing Your Clarinet

When putting your Clarinet into the case, make sure that you have loosened the mouthpiece ligature to stop it warping. Also don't forget to take the reed out and wash and dry it properly, then place it in the reed holder.

Keeping Your Clarinet Clean

After using your Clarinet, make sure that you wipe the keys, rods and wood with a cloth. Clean the inside thoroughly with your weighted cloth as wood may easily rot.

Make sure that you wash the mouthpiece regularly with warm soapy water, then rinse and dry.

Use your artist's paintbrush to clean the keys and rods.

To avoid the screws, springs and keys developing rust you should use a drop of oil. This will also help you with sticking keys, but don't get any oil on the pads.

A Guide to Notation

Note and Rest Values

This chart shows the most commonly used note values and rests.

Name of note (UK)	Semibreve	Minim	Crotchet	Quaver	Semiquaver
Name of note (USA)	Whole note	Half note	Quarter note	Eighth note	Sixteenth note
Note symbol	𝅝	𝅗𝅥	𝅘𝅥	𝅘𝅥𝅮	𝅘𝅥𝅯
Rest symbol	▬	▬	𝄽	𝄾	𝄿
Value per beats	4	2	1	1/2	1/4

Repeat Bars

When you come to a double dotted bar, you should repeat the music between the beginning of the piece and the repeat mark.

When you come to a repeat bar you should play again the music that is between the two dotted bars.

First, second and third endings

The first time through you should play the first ending until you see the repeat bar. Play the music again and skip the first time ending to play the second time ending, and so on.

D.C. (Da Capo)

When you come to this sign you should return to the beginning of the piece.

D.C. al Fine

When this sign appears, go back to the beginning and play through to the *Fine* ending marked. When playing a *D.C. al Fine*, you should ignore all repeat bars and first time endings.

D.S. (Dal Segno)

Go back to the 𝄋 sign.

D.S. al Fine

Go to the sign 𝄋 and play the ending labelled *(Fine)*.

D.S. al Coda

Repeat the music from the 𝄋 sign until the ⊕ or *To Coda* signs, and then go to the coda sign. Again, when playing through a *D. 𝄋 al Coda*, ignore all repeats and don't play the first time ending.

Accidentals

Flat ♭ - When a note has a flat sign before it, it should be played a semi tone lower.

Sharp ♯ - When a note has a sharp sign before it, it should be played a semi tone higher.

Natural ♮ - When a note has a natural sign before it, it usually indicates that a previous flat or sharp has been cancelled and that it should be played at its actual pitch.

Bar Numbers

Bar numbers are used as a method of identification, usually as a point of reference in rehearsal. A bar may have more than one number if it is repeated within a piece.

Pause Sign

A pause is most commonly used to indicate that a note/chord should be extended in length at the player's discretion. It may also indicate a period of silence or the end of a piece.

Dynamic Markings

Dynamic markings show the volume at which certain notes or passages of music should be played. For example

pp	= very quiet	*mf*	= moderately loud
p	= quiet	*f*	= loud
mp	= moderately quiet	*ff*	= very loud

Time Signatures

Time signatures indicate the value of the notes and the number of beats in each bar. The top number shows the number of beats in the bar and the bottom number shows the value of the note.

SWING WHEN YOU'RE WINNING

is now available in these instrumental arrangements

Flute	*9591A*
Clarinet	*9592A*
Alto Sax	*9593A*
Tenor Sax	*9594A*
Trumpet	*9595A*
Violin	*9596A*
Piano	*9597A*

I WILL TALK AND HOLLYWOOD WILL LISTEN

MACK THE KNIFE

SOMETHIN' STUPID

DO NOTHIN' TILL YOU HEAR FROM ME

IT WAS A VERY GOOD YEAR

STRAIGHTEN UP AND FLY RIGHT

WELL, DID YOU EVAH

MR. BOJANGLES

ONE FOR MY BABY

THINGS

AIN'T THAT A KICK IN THE HEAD

THEY CAN'T TAKE THAT AWAY FROM ME

HAVE YOU MET MISS JONES?

ME AND MY SHADOW
(AS PERFORMED BY SAMMY DAVIS, JR. AND FRANK SINATRA)

BEYOND THE SEA

Available from all good music shops

 www.robbiewilliams.com